CW00402824

The Genesis Roadshow

A play to be performed, read or taped

Ian Sharp

Edward Arnold

© Ian Sharp 1981

First published 1981 by
Edward Arnold (Publishers) Ltd
41 Bedford Square
London WC1B 3DQ

British Library Cataloguing in Publication Data

Sharp, Ian
   The Genesis Roadshow.
   I. Title
   822'.914   PR6069.434/

ISBN 0-7131-0615-8

All Rights Reserved. No part of this publication may be reproduced, stored in a retrieval system, or transmitted in any form or by any means, electronic, mechanical, photocopying, recording or otherwise, without prior permission of Edward Arnold (Publishers) Ltd.

This play is copyright. Permission must be obtained for all performances and recordings except when the performance is for an exclusively school audience. Application should be made to Edward Arnold (Publishers) Ltd., 41 Bedford Square, London WC1B 3DQ.

Text set in IBM 10pt Century by 🠖\ Tek-Art, Croydon, Surrey and printed in Great Britain by Photobooks (Bristol) Ltd. Barton Manor, St. Philips, Bristol.

Introduction to the Teacher

The Genesis Roadshow has proved successful and stimulating both as a production script and also as a play for use within the classroom. It is of interest to a wide ability and age range.

What makes the play particularly attractive to school producers is its flexibility in casting. There are a considerable number of permutations possible, enabling the play to be performed by as few as twelve or as many as thirty actors. There are in fact seventeen separate parts which are challenging and interesting as well as a number of smaller roles which can be combined to give actors the chance to make a major contribution to a production. Most characters in the play, with obvious exceptions, can be played by males or females thus extending the possibilities in casting. As all the action takes place in a fallout shelter, the set can be as simple or complex as a producer wishes to make it. More detailed suggestions for production techniques and ideas for extension and improvisation are to be found at the end of the book.

The play lends itself well to work in drama lessons. It can be divided into a number of self-contained units (separated in the text by asterisks) and thus a number of groups can work independently with the possibility of a combined presentation. There are opportunities for mime, music, singing and improvisation. The play can also be read in English lessons where again the asterisks might provide useful division points. *The Genesis Roadshow* can be discussed for its own sake in terms of ideas, character and motivation but might also be linked to a theme being studied within the English syllabus such as 'Survival', or simply to stimulate different kinds of written and oral work. The issues the play raises may equally prompt discussion relevant to the R.E. teacher's concerns.

Obviously teachers will use the text in the way they consider most beneficial to their particular students but there are detailed suggestions at the end of the book for possible ways *The Genesis Roadshow* might be used in the classroom.

The play is of interest to students from 14-18 years of age, although clearly its precise treatment would reflect differing abilities, ages and interests.

I.S.

The Cast

The Survivors
Clem
Mim
Petal
Narcissus
Survivor 1
Survivor 2
Survivor 3
Survivor 4
Several non-speaking survivors

The Outsiders
Godling
Myclog
Gablid
Mumpsy

The Cast of the Genesis Stories

Young Adam
Cow
Duck
Sheep
Bird 1
Bird 2
Chicken
Young Eve
The serpent as bus conductor
The serpent as shop-keeper
Mrs. Mephistopheles
Mrs. Flibbertigibbet
Cyril Lucifer
Pamela
Georgina
5 photographers
5 reporters
Disc jockey
Top of the pops audience
Old Adam
Old Eve
Cain
Abel
Sodom United fans
Serpent as leader of the Sodom United kop

Scene   A Fallout Shelter

As the audience takes its seats sporadic government information announcements are played over loud-speakers, explaining what to do before and after the nuclear attack. Once the audience have taken their seats, people are heard pleading to be let in to the shelter but being turned away by officials. The announcements become continuous and urgent. There is an explosion, then silence and darkness. The voices of survivors are eventually heard speaking from different areas of the audience, as the lights very slightly fade up.

CLEM SURVIVOR   It's over. It's over. Can anybody hear my
   words? It's over. It's over.
VARIOUS SURVIVORS (hesitatingly)   I can hear you. Yes.
   I'm unhurt. It's over. We've survived etc.
SURVIVOR 1   It must have happened. What we were dreading
   for so long has actually happened.
SURVIVOR 2   And we're alive. After all of it we're alive, alive
   here.
VARIOUS SURVIVORS (with a sense of growing hysteria)
   Alive. Here. In this darkness. Underground. Alive. In this
   darkness. Buried. Alive. Cut off. Alive.
SURVIVOR 3   And above us; can you imagine what it's like
   above us?
MIM SURVIVOR (amid mounting hysteria hurls herself down
   onto the main acting area)   Oh God, please God, make this
   not true! Make me wake up!

Enter GODLING, GABLID and MYCLOG. It is clear that they are entering from outside the fallout shelter itself. They are dressed flamboyantly; perhaps GODLING in top-hat and tails, MYCLOG in a bunny suit, GABLID in Bermuda shorts and sun glasses. Their nonchalant, expansive movements suggest massive self confidence. They are quite oblivious to the fact there has been a catastrophe. Their attitude to each other is good humoured. Their attitude to the survivors is loutish, even sadistic. Their entry quietens the survivors.

GODLING   Rubbish! Get her off! I want me mongeys back.

1

GODLING *pushes* MIM *back into the audience.*

GABLID   Godling quieten yourself. Thou art an embarrasquat.
MYCLOG   Not so Gablid. Godling hath reason. It is indeed a tinsy bit nacky.
GODLING   Well said, old Myclog. A pal of the old school.

They sit on separate tea-chests. At first they smile, then become a little disconsolate and finally stare vacantly into space. Enter MUMPSY who is dressed as an archetypal school-boy with satchel, cap, shorts, etc. He is always optimistic, always delighted and always looking for fun. He runs to each of the outsiders in turn trying to rouse them out of their lethargy but they show only impatience with him.

MUMPSY (to MYCLOG)   By the beginning. (to GODLING) From the beginning. (To GABLID) Under the beginning. (Unsuccessful MUMPSY sits down on the floor) Round the beginning. With the beginning. At the beginning. (Momentarily the three look up interested, they look at each other but shake their heads. They return to their lethargy.) Up the beginning. Before the beginning. Since the beginning. In the beginning.

The three react immediately, regaining their confidence and enthusiasm. MUMPSY beams.

GODLING   That takes me back.
GABLID   Golden days.
GODLING   And why not again?
MYCLOG (rising)   And the earth was without form.
GODLING (rising and moving past MYCLOG)   And darkness was upon the face of the deep.
GABLID (rising)   It would mean dressing up.
MUMPSY (rising)   Somewhere over the rainbow.
GODLING   And the spirit of Godling moved upon the face of the waters.
MUMPSY (dancing and addressing the audience)
    O I am Mumpsy,
    Always been Mumpsy,
    Must have been born this way.

    If I'm Grumpsy
    Get thump thumpsy
    I only want to play.
GABLID   My ears are over-full with your awful scrumpsy. Shruck it.

2

MYCLOG   And Godling said.
GODLING   Let there be light. (Light suddenly fills the shelter)
    And there was light!
    (Singing)
        Hi everybody,
        It's so nice to be here.
        Calm yourselves
        There's nothing to fear.

        Put your trust in me
        There's always a way
        I'll teach you all
        An old game to play

        GENESIS
        GENESIS
        We've done it before
        So let's do it again
        GENESIS

    That's all there is.

*Break for dancing, a kind of robotic movement by the four
outsiders in which some of the survivors find themselves becom-
ing almost hypnotically involved.* GODLING *snaps his fingers.
They return to their original places.*

        Who I am is a mystery
        I spend my time making history.
        I've knocked about a bit
        I've had my share of fame
        Yeh, I was the one who
        Invented the game of
        GENESIS etc.
GODLING   Well now, what a hap doth hap upon us all!
MYCLOG   And how could this hap possibly happen?
MUMPSY   Has anyone a paper bag I could burst?
GABLID   I think, admit we must, Endsy Worldsy!
GODLING   Just so, Endsy Worldsy. Above us the hush of
    death. And here we have the last remaining members of the
    human race . . . So, any questions? No? Good. In that case
    let us proceed to the distribution of ice creams.

MYCLOG *and* GABLID *offer their wares to the audience.*

MYCLOG   Vanilla, raspberry ripple.
GABLID   Chocolate or lime.
MUMPSY   I like them with nutses in.

MYCLOG   Tangerine, strawberry.

SURVIVOR 1   What you were saying just now. There might
    be other fallout shelters with survivors like us. You can't know
    we're the only ones left.

MYCLOG   But we've been.

GABLID   And we've seen.

GODLING   And in all truth the slate is clean. Not a breath of
    life could we find.

SURVIVOR 2   You telling us you've been and you've seen?
    You'd be dead wouldn't you? Radiation'd kill you wouldn't
    it? Cracked or liars, or both.

GODLING   Yet here we are, aren't we? You can't deny that.
    We weren't here before and yet we're here now. How did we
    get here? Where did we come from? Try asking yourself that.
    Tell them Mumpsy.

MUMPSY (to audience)
        When I jumpsy
        I'm so clumpsy
        Could I stop and play?

        If you likesy,
        You can ride my bikesy
        If you'll only let me play.

GODLING, GABLID *and* MYCLOG *applaud* MUMPSY *who
acknowledges by bowing.*

SURVIVOR 3   Who are you?

VARIOUS SURVIVORS   What are they? It's impossible. They'll
    contaminate us. Maybe they've come to save us all.

SURVIVOR 4   We're in a state of shock. They're an hallucina-
    tion, a delusion.

MYCLOG *goes menacingly into the audience and fetches out the
frightened* SURVIVOR 4.

MYCLOG   O pretty lady, if I were to twist your arm very hard,
    and I do twist arms very hard, you would have to agree that I
    exist.

As MYCLOG *proves the point,* MIM *the survivor launches herself
at* GODLING's *feet.*

MIM   Oh father, father, save me. I know you. I recognise you.
    I'm the only one. Remember that I'm the only one who knows
    you. Help me, you who are all powerful, I prayed to you, dear
    sweet God, and now you've come to take me back to the

4

world I left behind.

While the outsiders enjoy various forms of obeisance from MIM,
*2 survivors who are sitting next to each other among the audience
speak.*

SURVIVOR/PETAL   I don't really understand what's going on.
   Would somebody like to hold my hand?
SURVIVOR/NARCISSUS   I will, if you like, but you must
   promise not to let anyone else hold it.
PETAL   All right.
GABLID (to MIM who retreats back to the audience)   You give
   me the neck pain so trolls to you.
GODLING (to audience)   Now lovely people, this is all very
   fine and maybe not so fine, because although I admit I did say
   you were the last people alive you are now also the first people
   on the earth as well, lovey doves.
MYCLOG   And you see what we do is rather important. Now
   has anyone any ideas?
MUMPSY   I want to play a game.
GABLID   Now despite all appearancequeues Mumpsy is a Jean
   genius.
MYCLOG   For what else can we do here in a fallout shelter for
   perhaps eternity or until our food runs out, but play a game.
GODLING   And what better or more fitting game is there than
   the game of Genesis? Now whether you think I am God or
   not . . .
MIM   Yes Lord! Yes Lord!
GODLING (dismissively)   Whether you do or not — for the
   purposes of the game accept me as God and we shall try to
   start to live again in the only way that has ever been tried and
   tested.
GABLID   So ladies and gentlemen, step this way. Can you
   afford to miss the chance of a lifetime — to play your part in
   a second Genesis?
GODLING   A recreation so to speak.

*There is a pause until one of the survivors takes a tentative step
forward.*

SURVIVOR   Well I mean what can you lose? You've got to
   sometimes, haven't you? When it comes down to it, well, what
   else can you do?
GABLID   Thank you, sir. Myclog will take you to the back
   and show you what's what.

MYCLOG *escorts him to the back of the acting area and comes back to escort other survivors who gradually have made the decision to be in Genesis. They form a group sitting at the back of the acting area.*

GABLID   Thank you, madam, thank you, sir, just imagine what your neighbours would have thought. Thank you sir, etc.

CLEM/SURVIVOR (from his seat in audience to GODLING) I know you for what you are. I know where you lead and I shall not follow. I'm telling you I most definitely reject this path of folly. I shall dance the dance with the true God who for your wretched information, still even in this dark hour, loves us, I will have nothing to do with this perverted playing at Gods.

MIM/SURVIVOR (from seat in audience)   Oh Lord destroy this blasphemer and let only the faithful live.

CLEM/SURVIVOR   Blasphemy! Yours is the voice of blasphemy that can call him God.

GODLING   Never mind him. He hasn't tried strangling me yet. He's harmless enough. Every system needs one of his sort. But I'm sorry ladies and gentlemen, we really can't take any more. We've all the actors we need just now, so I suggest you settle back, safe in the knowledge you are sealed off from the more unpleasant effects of the recent disturbance. Forget the past and share our Genesis.

GODLING *joins the group of volunteers at the back of the acting area.*

PETAL/SURVIVOR (from audience to NARCISSUS who is next to her)   Aren't you bored with holding my hand?

NARCISSUS   Perhaps I am. I'm not sure.

PETAL   Wouldn't you prefer to put your arm around me? I think I'd like that.

NARCISSUS   I hadn't thought about it really. It sounds quite a good idea. I'll try it.

PETAL   I would certainly find it more comforting.

NARCISSUS   There. (Putting his arm around her) How's that?

PETAL   Even better than I imagined. Are you enjoying it?

NARCISSUS   As long as you promise not to let anyone else put their arms around you.

PETAL   I promise.

NARCISSUS   Petal my love, wouldn't it be ever so much fun to be in that Genesis?

PETAL   But, Cis, the man said . . .

NARCISSUS   I don't care. They'll squeeze two more in. Come on, let's be devils.

6

PETAL   If you're sure.
NARCISSUS   Ooh, isn't this thrilling?

*They leave the audience to join the other volunteers. Lights go
down except for a spot on* CLEM *in the audience area.*

CLEM (song)
    I can't see the light
    That shines in the sky
    There are no trees
    And no birds flying high
    Darkness around me
    Confusion surrounds me
    But God who made Adam
    I know you're still there
    God who made Adam
    I know you still care

    People are worried
    They get eaten up by fears
    Like little boy lost
    They'll drown in their tears
    Emptiness scares them
    Suicide dares them
    But God who made Adam
    I know you're still there
    God who made Adam
    Will wipe away all despair

    Millions above us
    Lie dead upon the earth
    But amidst this destruction
    There's going to be rebirth
    We'll see insanity yet
    We'll hear profanity yet
    But God who made Adam
    I know you're still there
    For the good and the bad man
    I know you still care.

    God who made Adam
    For the good and the bad man
    God who made Adam
    For the good and the bad man
    God who made Adam

    I'm scared

* * *

Fade out on CLEM. *Up on acting area where stand* MYCLOG *and* GABLID.

MYCLOG   And the Lord God formed man of the dust of the ground and breathed into his nostrils the breath of life; and man became a living soul.

GODLING, *who plays the part of God, selects one of the survivors for the part of Adam by putting his hand on his shoulder and bringing him into the acting area. They mime the actions as the verses are read.*

GABLID   And the Lord God planted a garden Eastward in Eden; and there he put the man whom he had formed.
MYCLOG   And out of the ground made the Lord God to grow every tree that is pleasant to the sight, and good for food: the tree of life also in the midst of the garden, and the tree of knowledge of good and evil.
GABLID   And the Lord God took the man, and put him into the garden of Eden to dress it and to keep it.
MYCLOG   And the Lord God commanded the man, saying:
GODLING   Of every tree of the garden thou may'st freely eat. But of the tree of the knowledge of good and evil thou shalt not eat of it: for in the day thou eatest thereof thou shalt surely die.
ADAM   Die? What's that mean — die? Don't like the sound of that word.
GODLING   It is not good that the man should be alone. I will make him an help meet for him.
GABLID   And out of the ground the Lord God formed every beast of the field.
MUMPSY   Oooh, I remember this bit. This is the bit I like the best. This is a good bit.
GABLID   And every foul of the air; and brought them unto Adam to see what he would call them.

GODLING *ushers in various animals and birds performed by the volunteers.*

GODLING   Okay.

Enter Cow.

COW   Moo. Moo. Moo.
GODLING   Well, Adam what you going to call that?
ADAM   Let me see.
COW   Moo. Moo. Moo.

8

ADAM   I know, I'll call it a cow. I don't know why. It just
    came to me. Is that all right? You don't think it sounds too
    silly do you?
GODLING   Anything you say Adam. You've got to live with
    it. Off you go er, cow. Next!

Enter Duck.

DUCK   Quack! Quack! Quack!
ADAM   Right. Yes. I'll call that a goat. It comes very easily to
    me really.
GODLING   Okay.
ADAM   No wait a minute. Make that noise again.
DUCK (impatiently)   Quack. Quack. Quack.
ADAM   Goat doesn't seem right somehow.
GODLING   Hurry it up. We've got quite a lot to get through,
    you know.
ADAM   All right. Hippopotamus. Yes. Yes. I'm much happier
    with that.
GODLING   Fine. Next.

Duck exits. MUMPSY *swoops in front of* ADAM.

MUMPSY   Ter Wit Er Wit Er Woo.
ADAM   Mumpsy.
MUMPSY   But I'm —
GODLING   Go on Mumpsy. No arguing. Adam's decision is
    final.
MUMPSY (to audience)   I'm Mumpsy. That's the bit I like.

Exit MUMPSY. *Enter Sheep.*

SHEEP   Baa! Baa!
ADAM.   Sheep and it'll be the same in the plural by the way.
GODLING   Just as you like, Adam. Next.

Exit Sheep. Enter a short-toed tree creeper.

BIRD   Tweet. Tweet.
ADAM   Short-toed tree creeper.
GODLING   Next.

Exit short-toed tree creeper. Enter red backed shrike.

BIRD   Tweet. Tweet.
ADAM   Red-backed shrike.
GABLID   And whatsoever Adam called every living creature,

9

that was the name thereof.

Enter a Chicken.

CHICKEN   Pok. Pok. Pok. Pok. Pok.
ADAM   Chicken.
GODLING   Right.
ADAM   I bet they taste nice too.

Exit Chicken.

GODLING   How do you like these creatures Adam?
ADAM   I think they're pretty good really.
GODLING   Is there any one of them that you think you could
live with, make a friend of, discuss your troubles with because
otherwise you're going to get a bit lonely just wandering about
on your own.
ADAM   Well to be frank. I honestly don't think . . .
MYCLOG   But for Adam there was not found an help-meet
for him.
ADAM   It would be nice to have another creature to chat to.
But I mean, you know, that dark and light you created.
GODLING   Yes, Adam.
ADAM   Well, I think it's a very clever idea and everything,
really neat but I think the nights, they're the dark bit aren't
they?
GODLING   Correct Adam.
ADAM   Well I just think the nights might get a little, as you
say, lonely. That's all. I mean the days'll be all right. I reckon
I could get to like the days, enjoy them, if you know what I
mean. Yes, the days are quite a pleasant prospect but the
nights, well, let's just say I've got my doubts about them —
the nights I mean. Some of those creatures, the one which
does that howling noise, what do you call them?
GODLING   No, what did you call them?
ADAM   Wolves. That's it. I called them wolves. Well, I think
they're great creatures, really well made I reckon, and
howling, well, I mean howling's a fantastic noise . . . in the
day. In the day I imagine I could really enjoy a good bit of
howling but at night — well, so if I could have a creature
specially made with the nights in view. I'm sure if you put
your mind to it you could come up with something. I know
you've been working really hard recently and I wouldn't want
to put you to any more trouble. But if you could see your
way to —

10

GODLING   I will do as you request but I hope you know what you're taking on; you might live to regret this.

* * *

GABLID   And the Lord God caused a deep sleep to fall upon Adam and he slept; and he took of his ribs, and closed up the flesh thereof.

GODLING *and* ADAM *mime the above.*

MYCLOG   And the rib which the Lord God had taken from the man, made he woman and brought her unto the man.

GODLING *brings on the woman,* EVE, *she is played by the survivor Petal.* GODLING *departs.* EVE *flexes her new body.* ADAM *wakes and stares amazed at* EVE.

ADAM   You've got to hand it to God. I could never have thought you up myself. Let alone make you. I mean looking at you maybe there is something to be said for those nights after all. Now I better call you something hadn't I? Do you make a noise?

EVE   Flippin' cheek! A noise! As much of a noise as you make. I haven't come here to be insulted you know.

ADAM   Yes, well I'm sorry. It's just that I've got so used to all these animals, but you're certainly different. I'll call you woman because . . .

EVE   Look I don't need you to name me, thanks very much. I've got a name of my own, I'll have you know.

ADAM   I wasn't aware. You see I've been asleep and . . .

EVE   Eve!

ADAM   I beg your pardon.

EVE   Eve. That's my name.

ADAM   I see. Well . . . hallo Eve.

EVE   Hallo Adam.

ADAM   Hallo. Yes — er — well yes — well yes, indeed.

EVE   What?

ADAM   Do you come here often — no, of course you don't, how silly of me. You've only just been created haven't you. Er, how does it feel only just haveing been created? How does it feel?

EVE   All right.

ADAM   All right? All right! Really? Good! I've been created quite a while you know. Yes, I've been created a good bit longer than you . . . Yes. You get used to it after a while.

EVE   Do you?

ADAM   Yes, it grows on you, so to speak. You kind of take it for granted, if you know what I mean. One minute there you are a bit of dust, or in your case one of my ribs, and the next you're created. You're somebody. It's funny really how quickly you accept it.

EVE   Is it?

ADAM   Oh yes it is. No doubt about it. Very funny . . . It's quite warm tonight, isn't it?

EVE   I wouldn't know, would I? I've only just been created, haven't I? I've got nothing to compare it to, have I? I mean for all I know it could be flipping freezing cold, for all I know. I wouldn't have thought that even you with your limited experience was in a position to start making pronouncements about the temperature.

ADAM   No, of course not. You're right. That's a good point you're making. You're obviously a very clever woman, but I suppose I shouldn't say that either should I, not having any other woman to compare you to. I mean, compared with other women you might be extraordinarily stupid. I mean I'm sure you're not . . . but, look, the point is I feel rather awkward. I'm not used to talking to women. You're the first woman I've ever talked to . . . Yes. But you see the strange thing is ever since I saw you I've had this very odd feeling, a kind of desire and I'm not sure what it is. I mean talking to you is very enjoyable.

EVE   Is it?

ADAM   Yes, but it's something other than that — this feeling I'm talking about. I'm pretty certain whatever it is begins with my touching you. How do you feel about being touched?

EVE   It sounds quite a good idea to me. Talking to you isn't very enjoyable, maybe this touching business will be more fun.

ADAM   Right! Okay! Now where to begin that's the problem. Where exactly should I touch first?

EVE   How about making a start with hands.

ADAM   Okay then. Here goes!

They touch hands. The survivor NARCISSUS *storms on from the back.*

NARCISSUS   You promised me, Petal, that you wouldn't let anybody else touch your hand.

PETAL   I know I did, Cis. But what should I do? I'm so confused. After all this is only pretend isn't it?

NARCISSUS   I don't care. You gave me your word.

PETAL   That is true. I did give him my word.

GODLING   All right. Billy Sillies. We'll skip the touchies.

MUMPSY   I like touchies. Much muchies. It's a good bit.

GODLING   Carry on Gablid.

GABLID   And they were both naked the man and his wife and were not ashamed.

NARCISSUS   That's it. I'm certainly not allowing my Petal to be naked.

MYCLOG   Stupid fellow. Naked have they been all the time. Pretendy Wendie. O gruesome grube.

NARCISSUS   Oh that's all right. She can be naked as long as she doesn't take her clothes off. I don't mind that.

CLEM (from audience)   It's a mockery, every piece of it.

GODLING   Now children. Uncle Godling will get cross. You have been chosen to play the Genesis game and play it you must or Myclog's feather will bring pains, cramps, tortures.

MIM (from the audience)   You have chosen us Lord! Chosen to lead us back. I believe in the goodness of the Lord!

* * *

MYCLOG   Now the serpent was more subtil than any beast of the field which the Lord God had made.

The acting area is now deserted by all except EVE *who wanders aimlessly around. Enter several of the volunteers imitating a bus.* THE SERPENT *is the bus conductor. The bus pulls up next to where* EVE *is standing.*

SERPENT   Hurry along there please!

EVE   What?

SERPENT   Hurry along there please. We haven't got all day.

EVE   Who are you?

SERPENT   Look, love, are you getting on my bus or aren't you?

EVE   Bus?

SERPENT   There you are standing by a bus stop. Well naturally we assume you are waiting for a bus. I mean, that's a reasonable assumption, isn't it? The whole bus system depends upon a general acceptance by the public of that particular assumption.

EVE   Bus stop?

SERPENT   Can you imagine the chaos there would be if there were massive queues of people waiting at bus stops none of whom wanted to get on a bus, or conversely that people just walking along the street expected buses to stop for them? I mean, it would require bus drivers with a highly developed degree of extra-sensory perception, wouldn't it?

EVE   Street?

SERPENT   Hop on. (Pulls her on board) Hold very tight there! Now where are you going, love?

EVE   I was only looking around and then . . .

13

SERPENT   New here are you?

EVE   Yes I've only just been . . .

SERPENT   Right, so where are you going?

EVE   I'm not going anywhere.

SERPENT   What are you doing on my bus, if you aren't going anywhere?

EVE   I don't understand what going somewhere means.

SERPENT   You having me on, dear?

EVE   I don't understand much of what you're saying.

SERPENT   Quite the little innocent aren't you? Look you were in Eden weren't you?

EVE   Yes.

SERPENT   Now just imagine you thought to yourself one day I'd like to be somewhere else. I'd like to be in another place. Right? Now however hard you wish it, you won't be in that other place, you'll still be in Eden. The only way actually to be in that other place is to go there. The only way to get there is by going there. There's no way round it. If you don't go there there's not the remotest chance you'll get there. That's what going somewhere means. Unless you go anywhere, you'll always be in the same place. Do you see?

EVE   Yes, I think so. But what I don't understand is why I should want to be anywhere else. Eden seems okay to me.

SERPENT   Eden's okay, sure it's okay, but maybe there are places better than Eden.

EVE   I'm quite content with Eden. I don't want anything better.

SERPENT   But that's all you know, see? You're just lacking in experience, aren't you? What do you know? Perhaps there are things you want that you can't get in Eden. You see, you just don't know. That's your problem.

EVE   Is it?

SERPENT   Yes, ducks, that's definitely your problem. So what's it to be?

EVE   I don't know.

SERPENT   Town Centre's what you want, I reckon. Town Centre's the best bet for what you want.

EVE   But I don't want anything.

SERPENT   That's what you think. What's your name?

EVE   Eve.

SERPENT   Look, Eve, I don't mean to be personal or anything but do you usually travel on buses without any clothes on?

EVE   Clothes?

SERPENT   I mean, don't you feel just ever so slightly embarrassed heading off for town on a public corporation bus absolutely starkers? Not that I'm objecting, mind you. You're a very lovely young woman if I may say so, but well, when you

14

get to town it's bound to cause a bit of a stir.
EVE   Really?
SERPENT   Oh yes. In all my years on the buses I've never had a naked woman as a passenger before, nor a naked man as a matter of fact. I thought when I saw you at the bus stop that it was a bit odd but I didn't say anything. Some people might think you were a bit of an exhibitionist displaying your body like that.
EVE   What do you mean? I don't understand. What's wrong with my body? There's nothing wrong with it.
SERPENT   Ah, this is your stop. Never mind. Enjoy your stay.

* * *

The SERPENT *helps* EVE *off. The bus disappears.* EVE *stands alone in semi-darkness. Gradually there is a build up of noise around her. It is taunting manic laughter mixed with phrases like 'Disgusting creature', 'Exhibiting her body like that', 'Body', 'No sense of shame', etc. It mounts to a climax and* EVE *turns as if trying to cover herself, sheltering herself from verbal blows. Suddenly the noise cuts out. Lights come up and the* SERPENT *is before her as a shop assistant.* EVE *though is still screaming 'Stop it! Stop it!'*

SERPENT   Good morning, madam, can I help you?
EVE (startled)   What? Look I'd like to get back to Eden as soon as possible. I came here by bus and I thought probably that meant I could get back there by bus.
SERPENT   Yes, of course you can. There's a bus stop just outside the shop.
EVE   Good. Well I'll go and get it.
SERPENT   Unfortunately the bus isn't due for another hour. But madam is welcome to wait in the shop here. I think we're due for some rain very shortly.
EVE   Shop?
SERPENT   Yes.
EVE   I don't understand what a shop is. I woke up this morning in Eden and I'm beginning to realise I was very happy there and then I met this strange man who took me away from Eden on something called a bus. He looked rather like you.
SERPENT   Ah, that will be my brother Be-elzibah. He's a bus conductor. A disappointment to us all. Rather the white sheep of the family, you know.
EVE   And he's confused me. It all seemed so simple and clear.
SERPENT   You're new here.
EVE   Yes.
SERPENT   Madam, welcome to Satan's General Stores. We sell

everything from bath towels to bananas, from fridges to crazy paving. Fruit our speciality. Our motto is 'mind your own business,' and our business is customers and our customers' business is our business. Now what exactly is it that Madam wants?

EVE   I don't want anything.

SERPENT   There must be something in our shop that madam could take a fancy to. Look round the shelves. We've everything from aprons to asbestos, from trays to tiaras and from airing-cupboards to aeroplanes.

EVE   Really I can't see anything here that I in the least wish to have.

SERPENT   If ready cash is a problem and looking at Madam I can see she is not in the habit of carrying much around with her, our credit terms are second to none.

EVE   Look, in Eden we have everything we need. These things you have seem really stupid to me. I can't see why anybody should need them.

SERPENT   Ah, but Madam doesn't seem to understand that what you need and what you want are quite different. Our whole business depends upon that difference. Now take our range of fruits. We stock everything in and out of season.

EVE   In The Garden of Eden we've got a fantastic orchard. There's more fruit than Adam and I can eat between us.

SERPENT   And your Landlord allows you to eat the fruit, does he?

EVE   Oh yes.

SERPENT   What, all of it?

EVE   Yes, well almost.

SERPENT   Look I don't want to waste your time, Madam. I can see you're a most perspicacious lady. Tell you what! We've just had a consignment of Knowledge Fruit in. We keep it by for special customers normally but I'd be prepared to make an exception for once.

EVE   Ah well!

SERPENT   Ever had Knowledge Fruit have you?

EVE   No, not exactly.

SERPENT   Try one then.

EVE   I really don't think . . .

SERPENT   You haven't been put off by these silly rumours that they're poisonous have you? I'd have thought a modern young woman like you . . .

EVE   I had heard.

Enter MRS FLIBBERTIGIBBET *and* MRS. MEPHISTOPHELES.

SERPENT   Excuse me a minute. Morning Mrs. Flibbertigibbet.

16

MRS. F.   Morning Mr. Satan.

SERPENT   Morning Mrs. Mephistopheles.

MRS. M.   Morning Mr. Satan.

SERPENT   Now ladies, what can I do for you?

MRS. F.   We wondered if — Ooooh, Ooooh. There's a naked woman in your shop Mr. Satan. She's just standing there all naked.

MRS. M.   Ooooh, yes so she is. Not a stitch to cover her embarrassment.

SERPENT   Ah yes, well the lady was just trying on some clothes and the fitting room collapsed around her.

MRS. F.   I don't see no collapsed fitting room anywhere.

SERPENT   I swept it up.

MRS. M.   Disgusting I call it.

SERPENT   I suppose you wouldn't be interested to hear that a consignment of Knowledge Fruit has come in.

MRS. M.   Ooooh Mrs. F. the knowledge fruit's in!

MRS. F.   Ooooh Mrs. M. the knowledge fruit's in!

They dance round the shop shouting 'It's in! It's in!'

SERPENT   Here you are ladies.

He hands them some fruit. They grab it greedily and leave.

MRS. M.   Who'd have thought it? A naked woman in Mr. Satan's shop and he seems such a respectable man.

MRS. F.   That place is going to the Devil if you ask me.

Exit MRS MEPHISTOPHELES *and* MRS FLIBBERTIGIBBET.

SERPENT   You can see what they think of Knowledge fruit and they're very much alive, aren't they? I bet I know what it is. Your Landlord told you all this cock-and-bull about not eating Knowledge Fruit, didn't he?

EVE   In a way.

SERPENT   And you want to know why? Because he knows its effect is so tremendous that he wants to keep it from you. Some people are like that. He reckons that if you eat Knowledge Fruit you'll think yourself as good as him. It's class distinction; that's all it is. Now come on have a try.

EVE   Well, I don't know . . .

SERPENT   Go on have a nibble. What do you lose?

EVE   All right then, just a nibble.

SERPENT   Here you are then.

He hands her the fruit. She nibbles.

17

SERPENT   You see it's nothing so terrible.

Pause.

EVE   Isn't anything supposed to happen? I don't really feel any different.
SERPENT   Just relax. It isn't a sudden thing. Knowledge works on you gradually. It takes people in different ways.

Pause.

EVE   There's one thing, Mr. Satan. You don't stock any clothes I could have?
SERPENT   Why, certainly my dear. Let me see. What would suit, madam? I've got just the very thing. Try these on.

She tries on the clothes.

SERPENT   How does it feel?
EVE   It's a bit strange. A bit ticklish. (She giggles) I can feel myself go all goose-pimply.
SERPENT   You look magnificent.
EVE   Do I? Do I really? Yes, it feels quite nice. It makes me feel very graceful. It makes me feel like dancing.

She dances round the shop and then stops overcome by giggles.

SERPENT   It's nice to see a satisfied customer.
EVE   No, what I'm laughing at, what I'm actually laughing at is thinking about myself getting on a bus with no clothes on, coming in here to you absolutely naked and standing talking to you quite seriously and those women coming in. I mean, what must they have thought? What must they be thinking now? And the funniest part of it all is that I thought it was absolutely natural. The really funny part is that I didn't see there was anything wrong with it.

She is overcome by her laughter. The SERPENT gives her a farewell kiss.

SERPENT   Here you are my dear. (Gives her some fruit) Take a bag of fruit. Perhaps your husband would like to try some. Look your bus is coming. I've put my eldest brother's address in the bag. You never know you might want to meet him. His name's Lucifer.

* * *

Black out. Lights up on ADAM *entering.*

ADAM   Now then. It'll soon be dark. I've sown the crops, fed the animals. Those hippopotami really seem to love crusts of bread. I must remember that. I wonder where Eve is? I think I might try that closing the eyes trick. That was quite a discovery. To make the nights disappear, all you have to do is close your eyes, relax your body and the night vanishes and it's day. And I was so worried about the dark. Makes you wonder if I really needed Eve. No that's not fair. She knows one or two quite good tricks of her own. (ADAM settles down to sleep.)

From off stage EVE *is heard to call 'Adam! Adam!'.*

EVE (entering)   Ah there you are!
ADAM   Well, where else do you expect me — (Seeing EVE for the first time.) Eve, what's happened to you?
EVE   What do you mean?
ADAM   You've grown another skin.
EVE   Don't be so stupid. It's not skin. They're clothes. They cover up your body because it's wrong to let other people see your body.
ADAM   But I used to like seeing your body. Can't I ever see it again?
EVE   Oh yes, it's all right for you to see it because I'm yours. The man coming home on the bus explained it to me.
ADAM   What do you mean 'I'm yours'?
EVE   I belong to you and you belong to me but to let anybody who isn't yours see your body is indecent.
ADAM   Oh!
EVE   Don't you like my clothes even a bit?
ADAM   Not really.
EVE   What do you know anyway?
ADAM   I think I'm going to do that closing the eyes trick.
EVE   Since you've discovered that trick you do nothing else. You're very boring. Do you know that?
ADAM   Boring?
EVE   We never go anywhere.
ADAM   Go anywhere.
EVE   We never do anything. We haven't got any nice things here. It never crosses your mind to get an airing-cupboard or an aeroplane, does it? You think you're such wonderful company for a girl that she couldn't possibly want anything else.
ADAM   Airing Cupboard?
EVE   Don't keep repeating everything I say.

19

ADAM   But I don't understand what you're talking about. We've got everything we need.

EVE   There's something you don't understand: what you need and what you want are quite different. You didn't know that did you? But what do you know lounging around in your birthday suit? If anyone were to walk in here quite unexpectedly I'd be so ashamed. What do you know? I'll tell you, you know nothing. You even think this fruit is poisonous. That's what an ignorant fool you are.

ADAM   What fruit?

EVE   KNOWLEDGE FRUIT of course.

ADAM   Now Eve. Don't be silly. I told you what God said. We can eat anything, absolutely anything from the garden, except the fruit of the tree of knowledge.

EVE   But that's the only one that's worth eating. You great nit.

ADAM   How do you know?

EVE   Because I've eaten it, that's how.

ADAM   You've what?

EVE   I've eaten it and I'm still here aren't I? I haven't fallen writhing on the ground and died have I? God hasn't leapt down on me in a thunderbolt and turned me to a cinder has he?

ADAM   But Eve —

EVE   But Eve. But Eve. Look I've brought you some Knowledge Fruit to eat. Let's see you try it, or are you frightened that God will tell you off and give you a smacked bottom.

ADAM   I don't know what's come over you, you're not the Eve I know.

EVE   Because I've swallowed Knowledge, Adam, and that's why I can see the pathetic lives we've been leading. Try it, or are you afraid?

ADAM   It's not that I'm afraid. It's like God said, we mustn't, and Eve I don't think our lives are pathetic. When you put it to me like that, I think we're probably very happy.

EVE   So what harm can it do, swallowing some fruit? If you don't like it you can carry on living the way you are.

ADAM   But what I'm trying to tell you, Eve, what I'm trying to say, is maybe it'll be too late, then, maybe once I've swallowed the fruit there'll be no turning back, if you know what I mean.

EVE   You're frightened.

ADAM   I'm not.

EVE   You're terrified.

ADAM   I'm not.

EVE   YOU'RE . . .

ADAM *grabs some fruit from* EVE *and crams it into his mouth.*

ADAM   There. I've swallowed the rotten fruit woman, and I
just hope you're satisfied.

* * *

Black out. Lights up on the SERPENT *at a telephone with two
girls at his side, one mopping his brow and the other feeding him
with grapes.*

SERPENT   Yeh I've listened to your tape baby, and I've got
two cats at home make a more melodious noise than that . . .
And you too sweetheart! (He puts down telephone.) Throat
spray darling.
GIRL 1   Yes, Mr. Lucifer.

Girl sprays liquid into his mouth.

SERPENT   You know, girl, maybe I'm getting old, but I'm
losing hope . . . Well don't just stand there gaping, you dumb
blonde, say something.
GIRL 1   Are you really Mr. Lucifer?
GIRL 2   Why are you losing hope Mr. Lucifer?
LUCIFER   I'm losing hope that I'll ever discover a really
original act, maybe every agent only makes one great discovery
and I've made mine. Maybe there'll never be another group
like 'Decaying Teeth'.
GIRL 1   Oh don't say that, Mr. Lucifer.
LUCIFER   Why the hell shouldn't I say it, if I want to, you
empty headed piece of flesh? If I want to say it, I'll damn
well say it. Now you've got me excited. Give me two of my
blood pressure pills.
GIRL 2   Yes Mr. Lucifer.

There is a knock on the door.

LUCIFER   Yes.

ADAM *and* EVE *enter.*

LUCIFER   Well?
EVE   Your secretary said we could come in. I'm Eve and this is
Adam. Your brother, Mr. Satan, said we should come and see you.
LUCIFER   Yes, of course. He telephoned me earlier in the
week, pleased to see you Eve, nice to meet you, Adam.
EVE   Thank you, Mr. Lucifer.
LUCIFER   Please. Please. Not so formal. My friends all call me
Lukey Baby.

EVE   Thank you, er Lukey Baby.

LUCIFER   That's better. Pamela darling.

GIRL 2   Yes, Mr. Lucifer.

LUCIFER   Get Adam some clothes to wear, he must feel cold standing there with nothing on.

GIRL 2   Right away, Mr. Lucifer.

LUCIFER   Oh and Georgina.

GIRL 1   Yes Mr. Lucifer.

LUCIFER   You better tell chef to hang on to my Hippopotamus a L'Orange. It looks like I'm going to be delayed.

GIRL 1   I'll tell him right now.

The two girls exit.

LUCIFER   Bet you got some funny looks coming down the street to my office, Adam.

EVE   Well you see Adam doesn't . . .

LUCIFER   Not that I don't think it's a good idea, Adam. It's a brilliant idea, very groovy indeed. Nudity as a gimmick, shows a lot of imagination on your part, Adam. But quite frankly I think you're ahead of your time. I don't think the public is ready for it yet.

ADAM   I suppose it is wrong to display your body. I didn't used to think so, Lukey Baby, but I've been thinking about it and your body is kind of private. It's yours, you own it in a way. You don't want to go showing it off to everybody do you. You see, Eve and I have lived a very sheltered life. We're learning slowly, but we sometimes get a bit confused. Maybe you could help us, Lukey baby. Coming up here we were talking and we decided what we wanted more than anything else in the world is an airing cupboard but the only problem is neither of us know what an airing cupboard is. Could you tell us, Lukey baby?

LUCIFER   It's happened at last! An original! A real original! What a hype. Innocence., I could sell that. Phone the B.B.C. the I.T.V. the C.I.A. A new innocence cult. Telegram Fleet Street, Lew Grade, Margaret Thatcher, Ron Greenwood. Lucifer's done it again. After 'Decaying Teeth', 'The Innocents'. Stay just where you are. I'm going to make you the brightest shining thing in the whole goddamned firmament.

Enter several photographers who surround ADAM *and* EVE.

PHOTOGRAPHER 1   Look this way, Adam. A big smile Eve.

PHOTOGRAPHER 2   This way Eve.

PHOTOGRAPHER 3   How about one of you staring into each other's eyes.

LUCIFER	Look innocent not lustful.
PHOTO 4	Let's have you holding hands.
PHOTO 5	Great.
PHOTO 4	Big smile, Adam. Not so sad.
PHOTO 3	Put your arm round her waist, Adam.
PHOTO 4	Great! Super! Let's have a kiss.
LUCIFER	On the cheeks, not on the lips.
PHOTO 2	Come on you can make it more passionate than that.
LUCIFER	They're supposed to look innocent, not passionate.

LUCIFER *drives off the photographers and ushers on several press reporters.*

REPORTER 1   Give us a bit of background, Adam. Tell us about your parents.

ADAM   Well you see — God . . .

LUCIFER   He's an orphan. They're both orphans.

REPORTER 2   Where did you meet?

EVE   Well —

LUCIFER   They met on a deserted beach at sunset quite by chance.

REPORTER 3   What's your favourite colour, Eve?

LUCIFER   White.

REPORTER 4   What's your favourite drink?

LUCIFER   Milk straight from the cow's udder.

REPORTER 5   When did you first start to sing?

LUCIFER   They used to sail up and down the river taking turns to serneade each other until one day they were overheard by a passing record manufacturer.

REPORTER 1   What's their ambition?

LUCIFER   To go to heaven. Thank you, ladies and gentlemen. Remember to stress the innocence bit. That'll be it.

* * *

Black out. Lights up on LUCIFER, ADAM *and* EVE.

ADAM   Lukey baby, we can't possibly sing it in public on television.

EVE   It took us weeks to get it onto the record.

LUCIFER   Don't fool yourselves. You don't think I'd risk using your lousy voices do you? We used a couple of session singers. We're using just your names and more important your image.

ADAM   So how can we sing it on television?

LUCIFER   You don't have to sing. All you have to do is mime and look innocent.

EVE   I'm not even sure I can remember the words. O, Adam,
    I don't want to go through with it.
LUCIFER   Now she tells me. Listen baby, I got too much
    money invested in you. Get out there. Mime, and above all be
    innocent.

Change to a top of the pops studio. A group is just finishing.
There are dancers etc.
Enter a disc jokey at the end of previous song.

D.J.   Well wasn't that a stinking piece of bromide. Only joking
    fellas! Loved it. Fantastic. Well now, music lovers, activate
    your auditory orifices for a brand new sound from a fabulous
    brand new duo. Yes, folks, it's 'Sweethearts When We Were
    Young' by the Innocent Twins.

ADAM *and* EVE *enter and mime to their record. During the song*
ADAM *and* EVE *make very obvious mistakes both in the timing*
and also often miming to the wrong voice and arguing between
themselves. Their movements are exaggerated and wooden,
suggesting they are simply doing what they've been told. From a
reasonable start there is a gradual build up in chaos which is
mirrored by the gorwing dissatisfaction of the audience who move
from contempt to outrage and finally they rush ADAM *and* EVE.
The riot is finally blacked out.

EVE
    Don't want to be sentimental
    But you're so kind and gentle
    It makes me want to cry Oooby Dooby
    It makes me want to cry.

ADAM
    Don't want to be starry-eyed
    But I want you to be my bride
    Until the day I die Oooby Dooby
    Until the day I die.

ADAM & EVE
    We've always been together
    Sweethearts when we were young
    We aint gonna part, no never
    Not until our lives are done.

24

EVE
>Don't want to be uncool
>But for you I'd break any rule
>To have you by my side Oooby dooby
>To have you by my side.

ADAM & EVE
>We've always been together
>Sweethearts when we were young
>We aint gonna part no never
>Not until our lives are done

>Sweethearts when we were young
>Sweethearts until our song is sung.

Black out. Lights up on ADAM, EVE *and* LUCIFER.

ADAM   Look. Look, Lukey baby, we're sorry.
LUCIFER   Lukey Baby! Mr. Lucifer to you.
EVE   It just wasn't our kind of song.
LUCIFER   What do you know about your kind of song. I
decide what's your kind of song.
ADAM   Maybe the next one will work out better.
LUCIFER   Next one. What makes you think there'll be a next
one. You've made me a laughing stock in the profession
You've ruined the good name of Cyril Lucifer Enterprises.
You're not innocent. You're just plain dumb.

* * *

Exit LUCIFER. MYCLOG *and* GABLID *resume the places they
had at the opening of this sequence, page 8.*

ADAM   It's all been your fault, Eve.
EVE   Go on, blame me.
ADAM   But we were so happy here once.
EVE   I know we were, Adam. But we didn't know we were;
that's the trouble. You only realize how happy you were once
you become unhappy.
ADAM   And it can never be like that again, can it? We can
never get back to what it was like in those first golden days. We
had perfection and we threw it away.
EVE   But we didn't know it was perfection.
ADAM   And now look at us! After everything we're naked
again. Those kids.
EVE   SAVAGES more like.
ADAM   Those kids ripped our clothes to shreds.
EVE   Our lovely new clothes.

GODLING (from off stage)   Adam! Adam! Where are you?

EVE   Adam, there's somebody coming and we're naked. We can't possibly let them see us like this.

ADAM   Quick. Come on, let's hide in the orchard. (They try to hide themselves among the audience.)

MYCLOG   And they heard the voice of the Lord God walking in the garden in the cool of the day and Adam and his wife hid themselves from the presence of the Lord God amongst the trees of the garden.

Enter GODLING.

GABLID   And the Lord God called unto Adam and said unto him:

GODLING   Where art thou?

ADAM *and* EVE *shamefacedly appear.*

GABLID   And he said:

ADAM   I heard thy voice in the garden and I was afraid because I was naked and I hid myself.

GODLING   Who told thee thou wast naked? Hast thou eaten of the tree whereof I commanded thee that thou shouldst not eat?

ADAM   The woman whom thou gavest to be with me, she gave me of the tree, and I did eat.

GODLING   Eve, what is this that thou hast done?

EVE   The serpent beguiled me and I did eat.

GODLING   Cursed is the ground for thy sake: in sorrow shalt thou eat of it all the days of thy life; thorns also and thistles shall it bring forth to thee and thou shalt eat the herb of the field. In the sweat of thy face shalt thou eat bread, till thou return unto the ground: for dust thou art, and unto dust shalt thou return.

ADAM *and* EVE *stand humiliated.* GODLING *turns to the audience.*

GODLING   Behold the man is become as one of us to know good and evil: and now lest he put forth his hand and take also of the tree of life, and eat, and live for ever . . .

MYCLOG   Therefore the Lord God sent him forth from the Garden of Eden to till the ground from whence he was taken.

GODLING *drives out* ADAM *and* EVE. *All three exit.*

GABLID   So he drove out the man; and he placed at the east of the Garden of Eden Cherubims and a flaming sword which turned every way to keep the way of the tree of life.

As GABLID *speaks,* MUMPSY *moves out to the centre, takes out his sword (or in his case a six inch ruler) and he turns every way as if guarding the tree of life. When* GABLID *finishes, he and* MYCLOG *exit leaving* MUMPSY *alone.*

MUMPSY (turning)   Roundsy! Roundsy! Roundsy! I guess you've all been wondering who I am. Well I'm that Cherubim with the flaming sword; well it's as good a sword as I could get, and I turn every way to keep the way of the tree of life. It's a pretty good idea of God's really. I mean who would suspect that stupid old Mumpsy could possibly be guarding the Garden of Eden. No one will ever find out. Unless you tell them.

MUMPSY *takes up his official stance.*

O I am Mumpsy
Always been Mumpsy,
Must have been born this way.

If I'm grumpsy,
Get thump thumpsy (Whacks himself with Sword)
I only want to play.

Slow fade out. The lights come up again and in the pause before the next action CLEM *leaps to his feet in the audience.*

* * *

CLEM   None of you dare face the truth. There has been a nuclear war. We are in a fallout shelter. The world as we know it has ended. It's over. Face it. This Godling is just a false path, leave it. There is a meter here on the wall measuring the level of radioactivity outside. At the moment it is registering a massively lethal intensity. That is the reality. Everything you're seeing here is just delusion.

GODLING, GABLID, MYCLOG *and* MUMPSY *enter rowdily dancing the tango.*

GODLING   What's everybody looking so serious about. It's not the end of the world, you know. Well, not quite anyway.
MIM (from the audience)   Great Godling.
GODLING   Yes, honeybunch?

MIM   I have been praying to you.

GODLING   Well how about that kiddeylugs!

GABLID   We are most highly grooblied.

MYCLOG   It regenerates our gunglies.

MUMPSY   I spy something beginning with F.

MIM   And I've also composed a hymn in your honour. It's called 'O Creator of Radioactive Dust'. Would you like to hear it?

GODLING   Well, how can I put it?

MYCLOG   No.

GODLING   That's it exactly.

CLEM   Listen, all of you. It's still not too late to put an end to all this. Look beyond fear to the love that is slumbering in all of us and you will find that the true God is still there for the taking. It has been given to us to make a fresh start for all mankind. We can do it on our own, accepting reality but in a spirit of goodness. There is no need to fall with him and wallow in the sewer of his imagination.

GODLING   What a dreary fellow. Do you know, I think he's beginning to grow rather fond of me. Funny way of showing it you might say. I don't care if they hate me so long as they love me. Love and hate's the same thing, and how many millenia is it before I get round to creating Sigmund Freud?

GODLING exits leaving MYCLOG and GABLID.

MYCLOG   And Adam knew Eve his wife (Enter old ADAM and EVE. They shake hands and sit down) and she conceived and bore Cain. (Enter CAIN.)

GABLID   And she again bore Abel his brother. (Enter ABEL.) And Abel was a keeper of sheep but Cain was a tiller of the ground.

MYCLOG   And in the process of time it came to pass . . .

Loud music drowns MYCLOG's words. CAIN manically and aggressively dances to the music, while ABEL appears to be involved with his homework. ADAM gets up and appears to turn off an invisible record player. The music stops.

CAIN   Eh, what do you mean by turning off that music like that? I like it.

ADAM   You call that music do you? I call it a ruddy noise.

ADAM returns to his seat.

EVE   Yes, Adam, you should take an interest in what Cain likes. You know what that man at the school told us. Don't take any notice of your father Cain, I liked it very much. What's the name of the group?

CAIN   'Death Rattle'.

EVE   Very nice.

ABEL   They're just the kind of rubbish he would like. He doesn't understand the first thing about music.

CAIN   I understand how to stuff those books of yours down your throat all right.

ADAM   I'm not having that kind of talk in this house. You can get out the pair of you.

EVE   Brothers will be brothers won't they? It's just boys' high spirits.

CAIN   I'll smash his skull.

EVE   The trouble is we don't talk to each other enough. We don't ever get together as a family and have a good old natter. There's nothing like a heart to heart to clear the air if you know what I mean. Get it off your chest, that's what I say. A bit of a chin wag. In the bosom of the family. Man to man talks. Tell it to your mum. Not parents but friends, chums really, people to go to for advice, an open honest atmosphere —

CAIN

    Sodom (CLAP. CLAP. CLAP.)
    Sodom (CLAP. CLAP. CLAP.)
    SODOM (CLAP. CLAP. CLAP.)

ADAM   Right that's it. You've gone too far, you foul mouthed layabout.

EVE   Don't be such a ninny, Daddy. That's Cain's team, Sodom United, isn't it darling?

CAIN   Yeh, and we're going to smash those Gomorrah fairies in the match, no trouble.

ABEL   They're just sloggers that lot, a bunch of animals. In the cricket match last Summer four of their side were out for golden hippopotami. No, if you want to see skill come and see Gomorrah wipe them off the pitch.

CAIN   Come over here and say that.

ADAM   All this fuss over a stupid game. Cor blimey in our day we had to make our own entertainment and it wasn't so bad, was it Eve?

EVE   Not in front of the children, dear.

ABEL   You're always going on about how good it was when you were young, I don't believe a word of it. I think it's all some middle-aged fantasy to protect you from the threat of the younger generation.

EVE   Oh isn't he clever!

ADAM   Good? How good it was. It wasn't just good Abel, it was ruddy paradise.

EVE   You shouldn't swear in front of —

ABEL   So what went wrong to spoil your paradise?

ADAM   We had you two rotten brats for starters and basically, how can I put it, we fell from grace. That's it, fell from grace we did. Very nasty it was, falling from grace. Wouldn't recommend it. Still it happens to everyone. It'll happen to you.

ABEL   It won't. You were weak. That was your trouble. Accepting that apple —

ADAM   Who told him?

EVE   You promised me, Abel, that you'd never tell Daddy I told you about it.

ADAM   You'd humiliate me in the eyes of my own son! You'd make me into a nothing! You swore you bitch!

ABEL   What does it matter? Family secrets, skeletons in the airing cupboards. I've known for years about it. Your life's a lie. You've tried to hide the truth from your children, pretended to be the big tough man and you took that apple, didn't you, like a soft little kid and because of that we lost paradise and live in this stinking hole.

ADAM   You'll do the same, Abel. I'm telling you for all your cleverness. You'll do the same. And has your mother told you everything . . . I bet she hasn't. I bet you've only heard her side of the story. I bet she never told you how she took the apple first from the serpent. Eh, did you?

EVE   Adam, I hardly think —

ADAM   There, I knew she hadn't. And as for you, Abel, you think you're so clever. I wish we'd never given you your education. I wish we'd sent you out to till the earth at the age I had to. See how you'd have liked that.

CAIN *lets out a great animal roar and rips up one of* CAIN's *books.*

ABEL   What the hell do you think you're doing?

ADAM   Let me get my hands on that vandal. I paid out good money for that book for Abel.

ADAM *makes a rush for* CAIN *but* EVE *intervenes.*

EVE   Now don't be hasty, Daddy. You've got to understand Cain.

ADAM   I'll understand him all right. I'll understand him right across the seat of his pants.

EVE   Now isn't it significant that Cain should choose a book on which to vent his aggression. We ask ourselves why a book? Why not your pipe instead, for instance?

ADAM   I'll tell you why not, I'd have broken his ruddy neck,
that's why not.
EVE   Not at all. Because Abel was dominating the conversation
and thus displaying his greater fluency of thought; Cain felt
himself intellectually inadequate. The frustration of not being
able to express himself overcame him, the need to show that
he too existed became a *sine qua non* for him and so he ripped
the book, the symbol, we might say, for the education and
intelligence which he was so forcibly being made to feel he
lacked. There we have it, I would argue.
ADAM   He'll have had it, you mean, if I get near him.
CAIN   I'm off, I'm off to the match. I'll see you there, Abel.
You're going to get what's coming to you.

Exit CAIN.

EVE   You're not going to the game too, are you Abel?
ABEL   Of course. You don't think I'd miss Sodom and
Gomorrah, do you? It's the game of the season. It symbolises
the eternal conflict between artistry and thuggery.
EVE   But they can be so dangerous, these games, the crowds
are so huge. I heard that at last week's match there were
twelve people watching. You could get crushed to death, let
alone the fights.
ADAM   Let him go if he wants to.
EVE   But it's not his kind of thing. He's such a clever boy.
ABEL   Yes, I'm a clever boy, mummy, and one thing always
niggled me. You've said you've always been completely
honest with me about the facts of life.
EVE   Of course I have. It's so important that a son should
trust —
ABEL   Well answer me this. You and Dad are supposed to be
the first two people in the world, aren't you?
EVE   Yes, you know.
ABEL   Well where do all the other people come from, eh?
You've just got two sons, Cain and Abel right? So how can
there be anybody else? It's not possible is it?

ABEL *exits*.

ADAM   I've told you before Eve, you spoiled that boy. He's
too clever for his own good.

Pause. EVE *moves amorously towards* ADAM.

EVE   Adam, we never seem to talk to each other these days.
ADAM   Rubbish. Course we do. We're always talking to

31

each other, don't talk such rubbish woman.

A longer pause during which EVE *continues her advances.*

ADAM   I think I'll switch the old telly on. Watch the match.

ADAM *gets up and apparently switches on a television.*

EVE   We don't seem to have anything in common. Really, I
sometimes wonder why we married each other.
ADAM   Didn't have much choice did we? The old telly should
have warmed up by now.

* * *

Lights down on ADAM *and* EVE. *Up on Sodom United supporters
including* CAIN *and the* SERPENT. *They are singing.*

FANS
Good old Sodom
Good old Sodom
We'll support you evermore.
Sod — om (Clap clap clap)
Sod — om (Clap clap clap)
SERPENT   Don't worry about it lads, so we lost. Who says so?
The referee was blind, the linesmen were bent, the pitch was
diabolical and what's more Gomorrah are a load of fairies. And
Abel's the queen of them all.
FAN 1   That offering was never fair.
FAN 2   Course it wasn't.
FAN 3   I mean a sheep!
FAN 4   Fancy tactics. Last week they tried offering a female
giraffe and they were reported to the League.
FAN 5   What's wrong with the fruits of the earth anyway? It's
always been good enough before.
CAIN   He's not beating me in this as well. Just because he's
got brains it doesn't mean he's got to beat me in everything
he does?
SERPENT   I told you it was fixed, didn't I? You got to
remember, Cain, when it comes to the old aggro, when it
comes to putting the old boot in there's no one to match
you. You're way out ahead there, Cain boy.
CAIN   Yeh I am, aren't I?

Enter ABEL.

SERPENT   Why look who it isn't. Hello Abel, old chap.

32

Awfully well done at the match today. Congratters. What!
What! Jolly sporting wasn't it? On the pitch, straight! (He
grabs him.) I'm going to beat your fairying head in.

ABEL (while being held)   It's all right. I understand you. You
probably live in a tower block, left school at sixteen, are
unemployed or at best do a boring repetitive job. I've read all
the sociological surveys, you know.

With swift efficiency the SERPENT *renders* ABEL *unconscious.*

SERPENT   He's all yours, Cain. Give him a bit of the old boot.
See you!

SERPENT *exits.*

CAIN (moving over to the unconscious ABEL)   Right Abel,
you're not so brainy now. This is for your 'O' levels — Maths
(he kicks ABEL), English literature (Kicks), Human Biology
(Kicks), Religious Studies (Kicks).

SERPENT *re-enters.*

SERPENT   Come on, Cain! You shouldn't still be here. Hey!
What you done to him?

SERPENT *examines the body of* ABEL.

SERPENT   You've done it now, Cain, you burke. Well it's
nothing to do with me, I didn't do it. Don't just stand there.
Run! You've killed him.

CAIN   But I haven't started on his 'A' levels yet.

SERPENT   Blimey! (SERPENT exits leaving CAIN bemused.)

CAIN   I don't even know what 'A' levels he's got.

GODLING (voice from off stage)   Hey you there! Let's be
having you!

CAIN   No not me, I done nothing.

CAIN *stands rooted to the spot as the following comments are
heard from off. The comments mount in a crescendo.*

ADAM   You've gone too far, you foul mouthed layabout.

EVE   That's Cain's team Sodom United, isn't it, darling?

GODLING   Stop! Come back here!

SERPENT   When it comes to putting the old boot in.

ADAM   Let me get my hands on that vandal.

EVE   You've got to understand Cain.

GODLING   Cain, give yourself up, come on!

SERPENT   You've done it now, Cain.
GODLING   Cain! Cain!

GODLING *enters.*

GODLING   Cain! Cain! Where is Abel thy brother?
CAIN   I know not. Am I my brother's keeper?

GODLING *drags* CAIN *to* ABEL's *body.*

GODLING   What hast thou done? The voice of thy brother's
    blood crieth unto me from the ground . . . And now art
    thou cursed from the earth which hath opened her mouth to
    receive your brother's blood from thy hand. When thou tillest
    the ground, it shall not henceforth yield unto thee her strength;
    a fugitive shalt thou be unto the earth.
CAIN   My punishment is greater than I can bear. Thou hast
    driven me out this day from the face of the earth and from
    thy face shall I be hid, and I shall be a fugitive and a vagabond
    in the earth; and it shall come to pass that everyone that
    findeth me shall slay me.
GODLING   So that nobody will kill you I will set a mark upon
    you, Cain, and people when they see this mark will not kill
    you but will dismiss you as stupid, lazy, criminally inclined
    and, to put it frankly, generally repulsive and whosoever shall
    come across your descendants will know them to be worthless
    and will scorn them and reject them or possibly write
    sympathetic articles about them in the expensive Sunday
    Papers even to the end of time.

GODLING *drives off* CAIN.

CAIN (complaining)   I just didn't get on with the teachers. I'll
    go to night school, day release!

* * *

Black out. Lights up on GODLING.

GODLING (to the audience in informal tone)   Now let me see,
    where are we? We've done Adam and Eve, Cain and Abel, yes,
    yes, and then there was rather a lot of boring begatting and
    begetting, better not bother with that, yes, yes. Ah good! I've
    been looking forward to this. This is where you all get involved.
    (To MYCLOG, GABLID and MUMPSY.) Thank you, palsy
    walsy.

34

MYCLOG, GABLID *and* MUMPSY *come forward. They adopt formal poses.*

GABLID   And God saw the wickedness of man . . . (GABLID breaks down into fits of laughter. This infects the others, until all four are giggling hysterically.) Look, I'm sorry. I'm always the same when we get to this bit. I just crack up.

MUMPSY (who speaks not as a little boy but as an actor who has been playing the part)   I don't know why; we've done it so many times and yet it still just . . . (He dissolves into laughter.)

GABLID (laughing)   It's the looks on the survivors' faces.

GODLING   It's the way I tells them. The only thing to do is to try and get through it as quickly as possible. Right? Are you ready?

They nod struggling to keep their faces straight.

GABLID (very quickly)   And God saw the wickedness of man was great in the earth . . . and that every imagination of the thoughts of his heart was only evil continually.

MYCLOG (fighting back the giggles)   And it repented the Lord . . . that he had made man on the earth and it grieved him at his heart . . . And the Lord said:

GODLING (caricaturing Hitler)   I will destroy man whom I have created from the face of the earth; both man, and beast, and the creeping thing, and the fowls of the earth for it repenteth me that I have made them.

There is no trace of laughter now. They seem confident and purposeful.

GABLID   But (GODLING wanders around the audience area) But, Noah (GODLING comes to CLEM and places a hand on his shoulder) But Noah found grace in the eyes of the Lord.

From this point GODLING *treats* CLEM *as Noah.*

CLEM (trying to remain steadfast in his seat)   No, Godling!

MYCLOG   Noah was a just man and perfect in his generations and Noah walked with God.

GODLING *forces the reluctant* CLEM *out of his seat and down onto the acting area.*

MUMPSY (running beside CLEM taunting him, speaking with the over emphasis of a bad child actor and using exaggerated gesture)   The earth was also corrupt before God, and the

35

earth was filled with violence. And God looked upon the earth and behold it was corrupt; for all flesh had corrupted his way upon the earth.

CLEM *has now been forced down onto the acting area where he is grabbed and held by* MYCLOG *and* GABLID. *He is unable to move.*

MUMPSY   And God said unto Noah.
GODLING (to CLEM)   The end of all flesh is come before me; for the earth is filled with violence through them. Make thee a fallout shelter of the sternest concrete and behold I, even I, do bring a flood of radioactive dust upon the earth to destroy all flesh, wherein is the breath of life, from under heaven; and everything that is in the earth shall die. But with thee (To CLEM) I will establish my covenant; and thou shalt come into the shelter, thou and thy sons (He gestures to Survivors) and thy wife and thy sons' wives with thee (He gestures to other Survivors).
CLEM   No Godling.
GODLING   And take thou unto thee of all food that is eaten, and thou shalt gather it to thee (Points to the tea chests) and it shall be for food to thee (To CLEM) and for them (To Survivors).

GABLID *and* MYCLOG *suddenly let* CLEM *go.*

CLEM (he addresses his words to the four of them but they appear to ignore him)   You can humiliate me. You can physically restrain me. You can even kill me. But you can't make me play a part in this farce of yours. I refused from the beginning and I'm not going to lose faith in reality now. So come on, do your worst!
GODLING   Was Noah saying something.
GABLID   He's playing the role very well, don't you think?
MYCLOG   Soon as I saw him I knew he was a natural; it was that air of authority.
MUMPSY (going up to CLEM)   Can I have your autograph, mister?
GODLING (to audience)   And may I take this opportunity of congratulating you all on quite outstanding performances. If I didn't know better I'd think you really were the actual survivors in Noah's arc. Somehow or other, you've managed to get that look of people who've recently lost loved-ones, whose whole world has suddenly crumbled about them, who have only physical suffering and mental anguish to look forward to —

SURVIVOR 1   Why don't you shut your filthy mouth?
SURVIVOR 2   Clear off, we don't want you.
SURVIVOR 3   We've had enough of you.

The unrest among the survivors grows. They are all shouting and jeering at the outsiders, calling for them to leave them alone. The outsiders seem to enjoy this response. Smiling they address the survivors and then in turn they exit.

GABLID   Thus did Noah (Exit) —
MYCLOG   According to all (Exit) —
MUMPSY   That Godling commanded him (Exit).
GODLING   So did he. (Blowing a kiss to CLEM, he leaves.)
CLEM (rushing to the point where the outsiders made their exits)   No he didn't! (There is an undercurrent of assent from the rest of the survivors to CLEM's words.) What do you think of that? He didn't do a thing Godling commanded him. He wouldn't even be Noah! He wouldn't even be Noah!

CLEM's manner suddenly changes. He begins to laugh oddly.

SURVIVOR 1   What's the matter?
CLEM   God above, do you hear what I'm saying? Do you hear what those snakes have trapped me into saying? 'Noah wouldn't be Noah' . . . 'Noah wouldn't be Noah' . . . me of the clear faith, me the rejector of delusions — 'Noah wouldn't be Noah . . . ' me of the true God, me the logical thinker standing here trying to say 'Noah wouldn't be Noah'. Is that how it's always been? Their laughter echoing down the corridors of history? Are they all there is, and all there's ever been?

CLEM buries his head in his hands. It is not clear whether he is weeping or laughing. Pause. MIM gets up from the audience area. She moves timidly onto the acting area. She moves nervously around the shelter as she speaks to CLEM.

MIM   I'm glad they've gone. They were liars, evil rotten liars. You were right. I'm sorry. I've been stupid. (CLEM doesn't respond) Look . . . we need to have someone to lead us . . . back. It's obvious now you're the only one who can. (She has moved to where the radioactivity meter is. She looks at it.) The thing that measures the radioactivity outside seems to be broken. Don't you think we ought to work out another way of finding out . . . if it's gone down?
CLEM (he slowly looks up at MIM)   Oh, is that so? I tell you what. I've had a wonderful idea, a really original idea. Do

you want to know what I'm going to do? I'm going to send out a dove.

CLEM *remains staring at* MIM. *She looks frightened and confused. Lights begin a slow fade. Just before the black out we hear the muffled but unmistakable laughter of* GODLING, MYCLOG, GABLID *and* MUMPSY. *Black out.*

The End

Production Techniques

The Text   The play has been performed successfully just as it stands but it would be possible for producers to incorporate the results of improvisations such as 1 and 2 of 'Suggestions for Drama' (see page 40) into a public performance if they were carefully edited; the fallout shelter scenes could be further developed by the same method. The play runs for about one hour and a quarter. There is the possibility of an interval on page 18 after Eve has left the serpent's shop.

Casting   Apart from the four outsiders all the other characters are survivors in a fallout shelter. The survivors act out the Biblical episodes and obviously each survivor, excluding Clem, acts out one or more of the parts. The survivor Petal must play Young Eve but that aside a producer can choose whatever permutation suits him or her best. There are in fact over thirty parts in the Biblical episodes but it would be possible to play them with as few as ten actor/survivors depending on resources available. The serpents can be played by one or four actors, Young Adam and Eve and Old Adam and Eve can be played by the same or different actors, Mim might or might not play a Biblical role.

Set   In the original production the whole theatre became the fallout shelter and the audience were made to feel they were survivors. Scenery was sparse and the atmosphere claustrophobic. The play can be and has been presented in many different ways depending on the acting space and the producer. The fallout shelter could be on stage and the audience quite separate from it. In these circumstances, the outsiders might well emerge from the audience and thus give an interestingly different perspective to the play. The only essentials are some tea chests containing tins of food and a meter on the wall measuring the level of radioactivity outside.

Costumes   Apart from the outsiders whose dress is discussed in the body of the play, the survivors could, of course, be wearing modern styles of dress. In the original production they began wrapped in blankets but when they participated in 'Genesis', they removed them to reveal simple, one piece cat-suits which distanced them and made the action seem more dream-like.

Music   Again Producers will interpret the songs according to taste and resources available but some suggestions might be helpful. *Godling's Song* has been effectively rendered by a kind of Rock Tango and on another occasion by a background of electronic effects with the words being chanted over it. *Clem's Song* is best delivered in the idiom of a simple folk ballad with ideally Clem accompanying himself on guitar. It could be sung unaccompanied and be dramatically powerful. *Adam and Eve's Song* will have to be pre-recorded and is a parody of the most hackneyed kind of romantic pop song. It might be possible to add a backing group for the 'Oooby Doobys' to heighten the absurdity.

Props   A producer will have to decide how realistically he wants to present the Biblical episodes. It is possible and effective to mime all props and merely by moving the tea chests suggest changes of scene, or, on the other hand, on the basis that under the auspices of Godling all things are possible, individual scenes could be created by quite extravagant props and settings.

Suggestions for Drama

If a full performance is not to be given, the following suggestions provide opportunities for more limited studio/classroom based drama, some of which could also be incorporated into a production.

1 The opening stage directions state 'People are heard pleading to be let into the shelter but are turned away by officials: Improvise this situation, thinking particularly about the feelings of the officials who know it would be dangerous to admit anybody else but who must seem inhuman to the desperate people outside. Try and build this scene up to the moment of the explosion.

2 Act out the reactions of a series of people hearing the news that there is to be a nuclear attack. There should be three stages to this:

1. Before — what are they doing or talking about? If it were particularly light-hearted it might create an effective contrast.
2. The moment itself — it might be an announcement on T.V. or radio, or from a member of their family, or gathered from the sight of people's panic.

40

3. The Reaction — You could read *Your Attention Please* by
Peter Porter in '7 Themes in Modern Verse' before starting.

3 Ignore the script up to the point of Godling's entrance and
improvise what you think people would say and how they would
act in the shelter after the explosion. End your improvisation with
the arrival of Godling, Myclog, Gablid and Mumpsy and then
act out the script to the bottom of page 5 when the volunteers
leave the audience.

4 Act out pages 8 and 9 where the volunteers perform the start
of the story of Genesis. Concentrate on the quality of your mime
for God and Adam as well as all the animals.

5 Act out the scene in 'The Top of the Pops' studio. It would
be best if a group of you could record on tape a version of the
song for Adam and Eve to mime to. Think about what kind of
actions Adam and Eve would use to present their song.

6 In pairs, improvise meetings between the only two people
alive on earth. They need not necessarily be the first two but
could be the last as a result, perhaps, of a mystery virus. Try to
involve an argument in the dialogue. You could read Thomas
Hood's *The Last Man* in 'Voices 2' before starting.

7 The match which Cain and Abel go to refers to the offerings
that each made to God as described in the Bible. Read the
passage in the Bible and then improvise the situation using the
characters of Cain and Abel as in the play. You might try to use
a presentation similar to that of 'Match of the Day' with
chanting fans, commentators, slow-motion replays, interviews,
etc.

8 The play is divided up into sections by asterisks. Choose one
section and put it onto tape. You may have to make some
changes to the script to make clear on sound what is happening.
For instance on page 4 where a sound audience would not know
that Mumpsy was bowing, you could make him say, 'Thank you.
Thank you.' during the applause to make the situation clear.
Try to find ways of avoiding simply having a narrator reading
out the stage directions.

Questions about the Play for Discussion or Written Answers

These are questions which need to be discussed by the teacher and class but which might lead to varying kinds of written work.

1 On page 16 The Serpent says 'What you need and what you want are quite different'. What do you think he means by that? Would you say that most people today in Britain have what they need or what they want?

2 What do you think Godling, Myclog, Gablid and Mumpsy are supposed to be? How do you feel about the way they treat the survivors?

3 On page 20 Adam says, 'I don't know what's come over you. You're not the Eve I know.' How do you think Eve has changed since Adam last saw her?

4 How does Cyril Lucifer treat Adam and Eve? Do you think pop stars in our society are exploited in the same way?

5 Eve says on page 25 'You only realise how happy you are when you become unhappy.' What does she mean? Do you agree with her?

6 In what ways are Cain and Abel different? You should answer some of the following questions about them: what kinds of music would each of them like; how would they dress; where would they go out on a Saturday night; what do you think their teachers would say about them? You could find more questions to answer about both of them and produce a file or report on each.

7 On page 34 Godling talks about Cain's descendants. Who are they today? Do they get a fair chance in our society or are they still cast out?

8 What do you think of Adam's and Eve's attitudes to their children? How realistic a couple do they seem to you to be?

9 How would you describe the different reactions of Mim and Clem to the outsiders?

10 How would you sum up Clem's attitude at the end of the play? Why does he seem to be both weeping and laughing?

Related Topics

The situation with which the play deals is a serious one; you might want to consider the subject in other ways.

1 What do you think life would really be like in a fallout shelter? Write a diary of a survivor, recording thoughts and incidents.

2 Write a play yourself based on the same situation and set in a fallout shelter. Concentrate on writing scenes which bring out the conflicts and strains. Do you think there would be any occasional moments of humour?

3 Imagine you were in a shelter where radio contact was made with another group of survivors; with a partner prepare the dialogue that might take place.

4 'Exodus'. Write in whatever way you feel would be most effective (play, story or poem) about what it would be like eventually to leave the shelter. Think about the hopes and fears as the time drew near as well as the mixture of emotions that would be felt on seeing the terrible destruction that would be found outside.

5 Draw a mushroom-cloud and fill it in with words and phrases connected in your mind with nuclear war. Use your ideas as notes for a poem.

6 Group work. You are a group of survivors in a shelter. The bombs have just been dropped. You realised you have survived. Discuss how you all intend to cope with the problems of your long stay underground both physically and mentally. Report back to the class as a whole.

7 Either in small groups or with the class as a whole discuss your views on the following questions: Is nuclear war inevitable? Will man destroy himself totally? Is disarmament possible? Should Britain have its own nuclear weapons? Do nuclear weapons prevent war? How does the possibility of a nuclear holocaust affect your belief in God?